Essential 8 Progress Tracking Sheet

	1	2	3	4	5	6	7	8	9	10	11	12	Summary
Green: All correct													
Amber: Some correct													
Red: None correct													
1. Transformations													
2. Area and Perimeter													
3. Probability													
4. Angles													
5. Percentages													
6. Ratio and Proportion													
7. Algebra Skills													
8. Straight Line Graphs													
Stretch question													
Challenge question													

C000095506

1

Welcome to your Essential 8 workbook (Book 1 *Revised*).

This is your book in which to practise topics which are most likely to appear in your GCSE maths exam.

Answer the questions in the spaces provided, mark them from the answer sheet and then fill in the Progress Tracking Sheet on page 1.

You will notice that the questions are always in the same order:

1. Transformations
2. Area and Perimeter
3. Probability
4. Angles
5. Percentages, fractions and decimals
6. Ratio
7. Algebra skills
8. Straight line graphs

There is a 'stretch' question at the end of each section which you may need to research and learn new skills in order to answer.

Then there is a 'challenge' question that you will need to use some higher level thinking skills to tackle.

At the end of term, you will have a personal record of your progress and you will be brilliant at all 8 topics.

Essential 8 Number 1

1A

1.

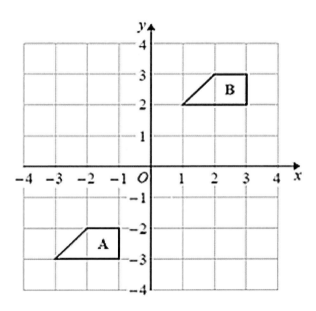

Describe fully the single transformation that maps shape **A** onto shape **B**.

2.

Find the area of the triangle.

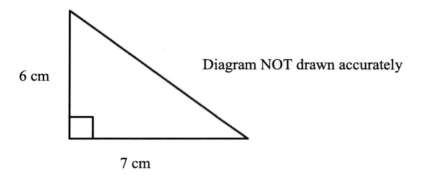

6 cm

Diagram NOT drawn accurately

7 cm

3.

In a bag there are three types of sweets.

There are

12 toffees

7 boiled sweets

and 9 mints

Annie takes a sweet at random from the bag

a) What is the probability that she takes a toffee?

....

Lennox takes two sweets from the bag.

b) Write down all the possible combinations Lennox could take.

....

....

....

4.

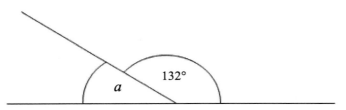

Work out angle *a*.

Give a reason for your answer.

5.

There are 350 buttons in a box.

30 % of these buttons are blue.

Work out the number of blue buttons in the box.

6.

There are 6 red counters and some black counters in a box. The ratio of red to black counters is 2:9.

What is the total amount of red and black counters in the box?

7.

a) Simplify $d + d + d + d$

b) Simplify $d \times d \times d \times d$

c) Simplify $3f + 4 - 2f + 6$

d) Simplify $2 \times e \times g \times 4 \times e$

8.

Complete the table for y = 3x + 2 for values of x from 0 to 4

x	0	1	2	3	4
y		5		11	

Draw the graph of y = 3x + 2 on the axes below.

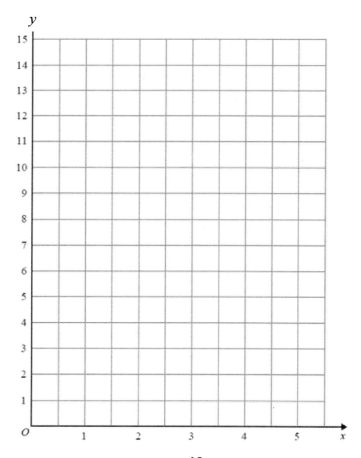

Stretch:

Here is a shaded quadrilateral within a square.

Work out the area of the shaded quadrilateral.

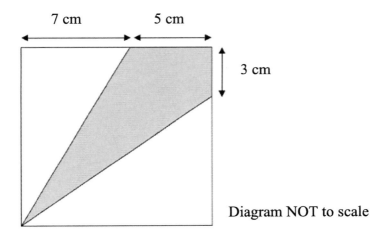

Diagram NOT to scale

Challenge:

How could you slice through a cube to form a cross section which is a perfect hexagon?

Essential 8 Number 2

2A

1.

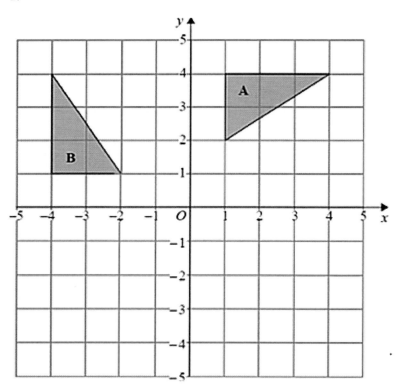

Describe fully the single transformation that maps shape **A** onto shape **B**.

2.

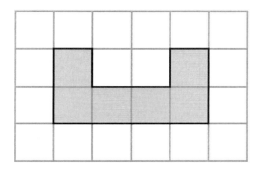

The shape above is drawn on centimetre squared paper.

a) Write down the perimeter of the shape.

b) Find the area of the shape.

3.

John rolls a fair, ordinary dice once.

a) Mark with a cross (X) on the probability scale below, the probability that John will roll a 6 on the dice.

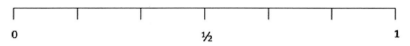

0   ½   1

Candice flips a fair, ordinary coin once.

b) Mark with a cross (X) on the probability scale below, the probability that the coin will land to show tails uppermost.

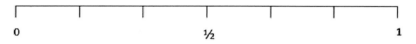

0   ½   1

There are 2 lime flavoured sweets and 4 strawberry flavoured sweets in a tin. A sweet is taken out at random.

c) Mark with a cross (X) on the probability scale below, the probability of picking a strawberry flavoured sweet.

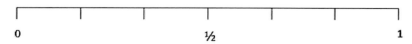

0   ½   1

4.

Diagram **NOT** accurately drawn.

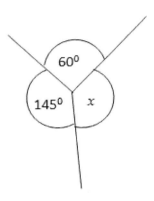

Find angle x.

Give a reason for your answer.

5.

A set of four chairs and a dining table normally costs £850.

In a sale, there is a 40 % discount.

Work out the sale price of the table and chairs.

6.

Anna is mixing sand and cement in the ratio of 3:1. She uses 15 kg of sand.

How much cement does she need to form the correct mix?

7.

   a) Simplify $5a + 4b + a - 2b$

   b) Expand $6(t + 4)$

   c) Fully factorise $4m - 8$

   d) Simplify $b^4 \times b^3$

8.

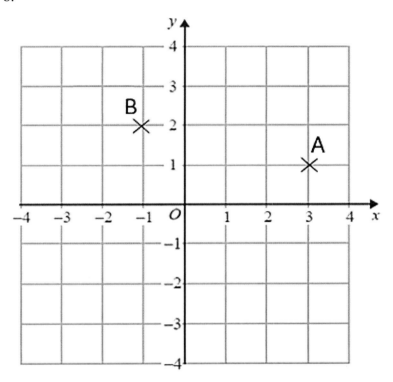

a) Write down the coordinates of point A.

b) Write down the coordinates of point B.

c) On the grid, mark the point which has coordinates (2, -3) and label it 'C'

d) On the grid, draw in the line $x = -3$.

Stretch:

Kelly invests £8500 for three years in a building society account.

She earns 3% per year compound interest.

How much money does Kelly have in her building society account at the end of 3 years?

Challenge:

There are 3 positive integers (whole numbers) whose sum (added together) is equal to their product (multiplied together).

What are the 3 positive integers which have this property?

Essential 8 Number 3

3A

1.

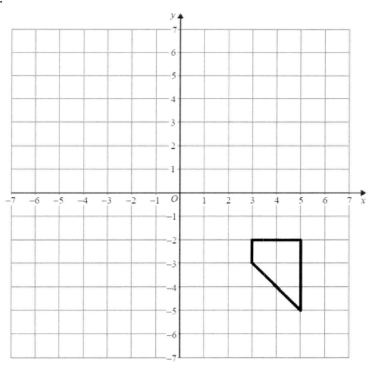

Reflect the trapezium in the line x = 1.

2.

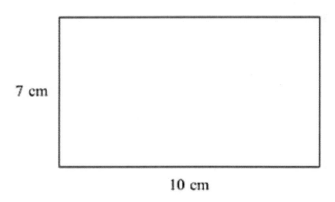

7 cm

10 cm

a) What is the perimeter of the rectangle?

b) Find the area of the rectangle.

3.

80 children went to the leisure centre. They either went bowling or they went swimming.

46 of the children are boys.

23 of the 80 children went bowling.

29 of the girls went swimming.

a) Use the information to complete the frequency tree.

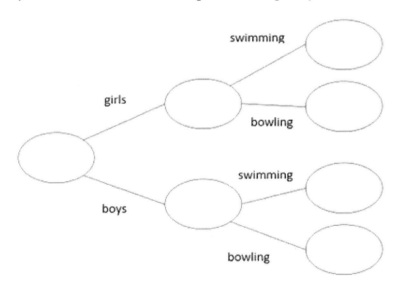

One of the girls is chosen at random.

b) Work out the probability that she went bowling

4.

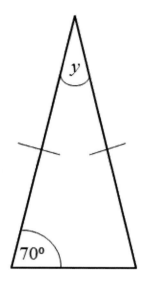

Diagram **NOT** accurately drawn.

Find angle y.

Give reasons for your answer.

5.

a) Write $\frac{1}{4}$ as a decimal.

b) Write 0.6 as a fraction.

c) Write 21 out of 30 as a fraction in its simplest form.

6.

Bert and Ernie share 220 cookies in the ratio of 5:6.

How many cookies does Bert have?

7.

Abigail has n cards.

Brett has twice as many cards as Abigail.

Chris has 7 more cards than Abigail.

They have a total of 35 cards.

    a)   Write an expression for the total amount of cards.

    b)   Work out the number of cards Abigail has.

8.

Complete the table of values for $y = 9 - x$

x	-1	0	1	2	3	4
y			8			5

Draw the graph of $y = 9 - x$ on the axes below.

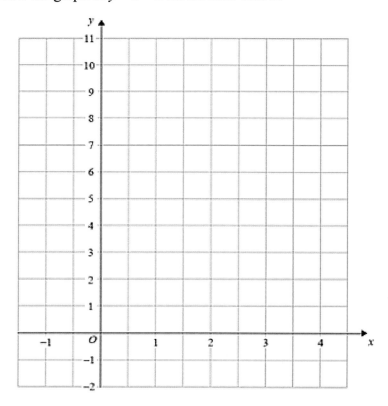

Stretch:

Omid buys a television for £280 in 30% off sale.

What was the full price of the television before the sale?

Challenge:

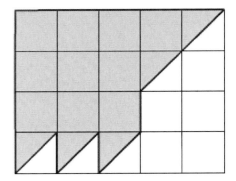

Describe the shaded region in the diagram above in as many different ways as you can

Essential 8 Number 4

4A

1.

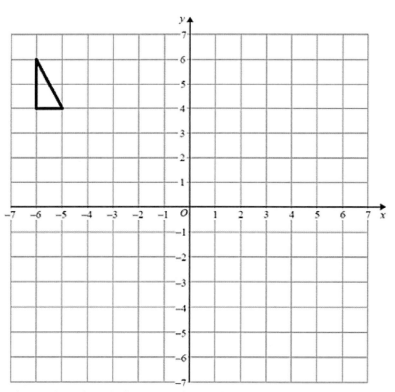

Enlarge the triangle by scale factor four from centre (-7,6)

2.

Find the area of this shape.

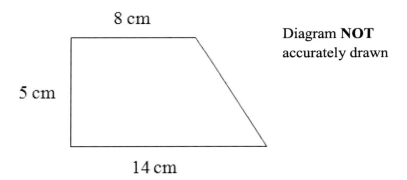

8 cm

5 cm

14 cm

Diagram **NOT**
accurately drawn

3.

Alex and Bjorn play each other at tennis and snooker.

The probability that Bjorn wins the tennis match is 0.6

The probability that Bjorn wins at snooker is 0.3

Work out the probability that Bjorn does not win either game.

4.

Diagram **NOT**
accurately drawn

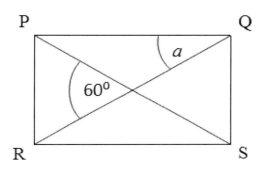

PQRS is a rectangle.

Find angle a.

Give reasons for your answer.

5.

Laura has £640

Harry has £480

Laura and Harry are each going to give 15 % of their money to a charity for pets.

Calculate the amount of money they will give to the charity.

6.

Rod, Jane and Freddie share £630 in the ratio of 2:3:4

What is the difference between Rod's share and Freddie's share?

7.

a) Expand and simplify $\quad 8a + 5(a - 3b)$

b) Simplify $\quad y^4 \times y^5$

c) Fully factorise $\quad 6d + 18$

d) Factorise $\quad 7e - 21$

8.

a) Complete the table of values for $y = 2x + 4$.

x	-2	-1	0	1	2	3	4
y	0				8		

b) Plot the graph of $y = 2x + 4$ on the axes below.

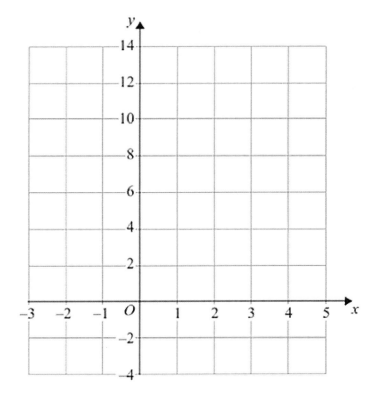

Stretch:

Can you expand these three brackets? $(x + 1)(x + 1)(x - 2)$

Challenge:

If the likelihood of rain tomorrow is twice that of remaining dry, what is the probability of wet weather?

Essential 8 Number 5

5A

1.

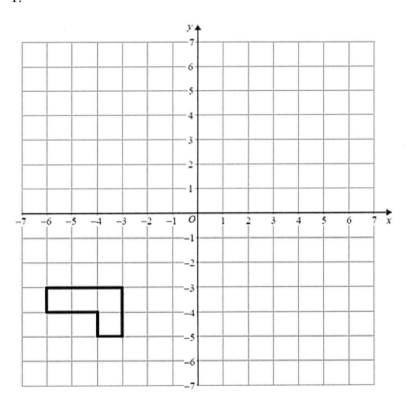

Rotate the shape 180º about the origin

2.

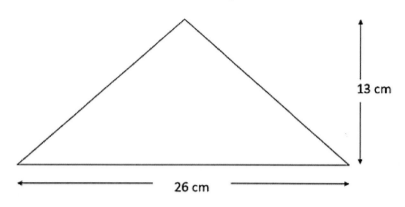

Find the area of the triangle shown in the diagram above.

3.

There are 20 counters in a jar.

5 of these counters are red and 7 are blue. The rest are green.

A counter is taken at random from the jar.

a) What is the probability that this counter is green?

b) What is the probability that the counter is not red?

4.

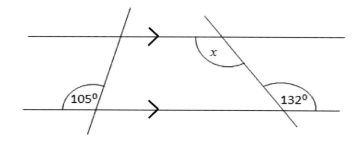

Diagram **NOT** to scale

Find the angle x.

Give a reason for your answer.

5B

5.

A ticket to a music concert costs £45 plus 20% VAT.

What is the total cost of the ticket?

6.

Alana is making 5 litres of orange drink for a children's party.

The concentrated squash and water must be mixed in the ratio of 1:9

How much concentrated squash does Alana need?

7.

Simplify

    a) $b + b + b + b + b$

    b) $c \times c \times 4$

    c) $8ef - 3ef$

Solve

    d) $4x = 32$

    e) $3h + 7 = 22$

8.

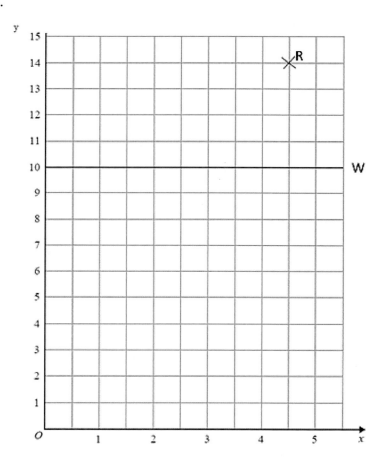

a) Write down the coordinates of R.

b) Plot the point (2,11) on the axes above. Label the point S.

c) Write down the equation for the line W.

d) Draw the line $y = x$ on the axes.

Stretch:

Lucy worked out $\dfrac{4}{5} + \dfrac{3}{4}$

She wrote: $\dfrac{4}{5} + \dfrac{3}{4} = \dfrac{4}{20} + \dfrac{3}{20} = \dfrac{7}{20}$

The answer of $\dfrac{7}{20}$ is wrong.

(a) Describe one mistake that Lucy made.

Challenge:

Simon worked out $1\dfrac{1}{3} \times 4\dfrac{1}{2}$

He wrote $\quad 1 \times 4 = 4$ and $\dfrac{1}{3} \times \dfrac{1}{2} = \dfrac{1}{6}$

So $1\dfrac{1}{3} \times 4\dfrac{1}{2} = 4\dfrac{1}{6}$

The answer of $4\dfrac{1}{6}$ is wrong.

(b) Describe one mistake that Simon made.

Essential 8 Number 6

6A

1.

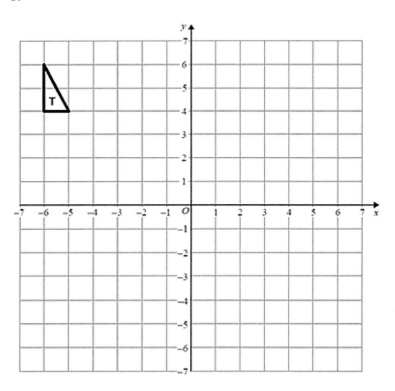

Rotate triangle T 90° clockwise about the point (-2,2)

2.

The diagram shows a rectangle with length 30cm and width 14cm.

Diagram **NOT** to scale

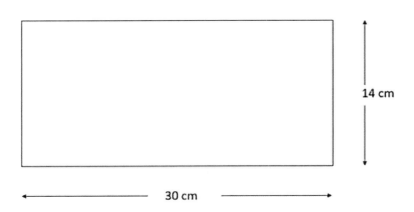

a) Find the perimeter of the rectangle.

A rectangle of card with the same dimensions is going to be made into a charity gala invitation edged with gold braid.

Gold braid costs £0.05 per cm.

b) How much will it cost to edge 100 invitations with gold braid?

3.

The probability that a new dishwasher has a fault is 0.018

What is the probability that a new dishwasher does **not** have a fault?

4.

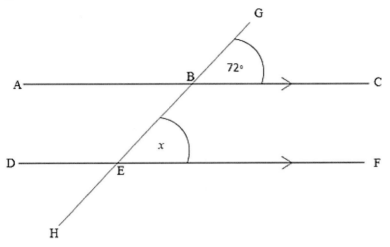

Diagram NOT accurately drawn

What is angle x?

Give a reason for your answer.

5.

Wendy is buying a silver necklace.

The necklace costs £80.

She pays a deposit of 40 %.

a) Work out how much she pays as a deposit.

The remainder can be paid in instalments of £6 per week.

b) How many weeks are needed to pay the full amount due?

6.

Omar and Julie divide the rent for their flat in the ratio of 3:4

Their rent is £840 per month.

How much rent does Omar pay?

7.

Simplify

    a) $t + 2t + 3t$

    b) $3e \times 2e \times e$

    c) $9qp - 4qp$

Solve

    d) $\dfrac{r}{3} = 8$

    e) $4b + 6 = 38$

8.

a) Complete the table for $y = 8-2x$ for values of x from -1 to 4

x	-1	0	1	2	3	4
y						

b) Plot the graph of $y = 8-2x$ on the axes below

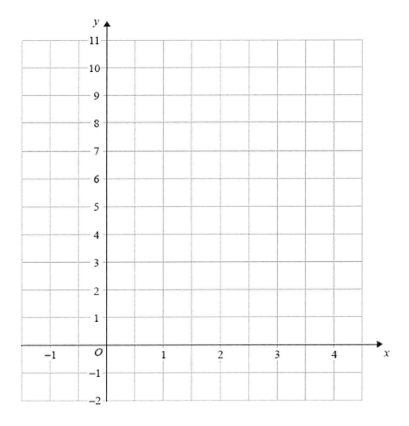

Stretch:

Solve the simultaneous equations

$3x + 5y = 4$

$10x - 5y = 35$

Challenge:

A square has an area that has the same value as its perimeter.

What is the side length of the square?

Essential 8 Number 7

7A

1.

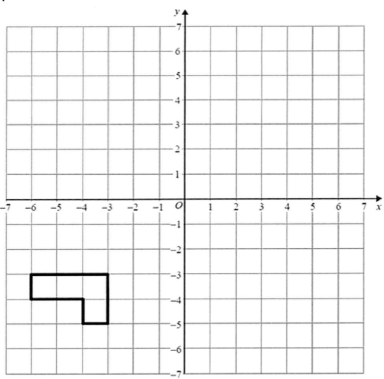

Reflect the shape in the line $y = -x$

2.

Diagram NOT accurately drawn.

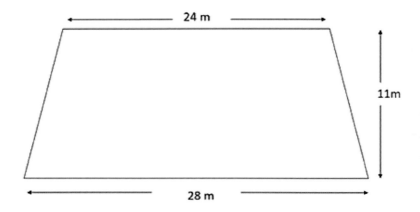

What is the area of the trapezium shown in the diagram?

3.

There are some boys and girls playing in the playground.

The probability of picking a girl at random from this group of children is $\frac{3}{8}$

What is the probability of picking a boy?

4.

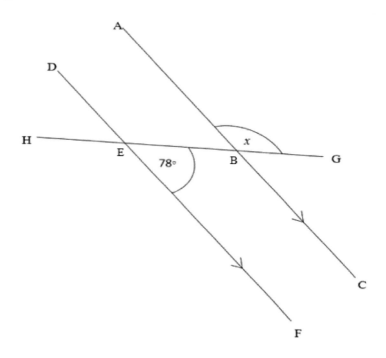

Diagram NOT accurately drawn.

What is angle x?

Give reasons for your answer.

5.

a) Write down the fraction of the shape above that is shaded.

b) Write this fraction as a percentage rounded to one decimal place.

c) Shade 60% of this shape.

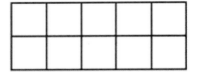

6.

A recipe for cookie dough states that flour, butter and milk must be mixed in the ratio of 3:2:1

a) How much flour is required to make 900 grams of cookie dough?

Marek wants to make 900 grams of cookie dough.

He has 250 grams of butter.

b) Does he have enough butter to make 900 grams of cookie dough?

7.

a) Simplify $5y + 4x - 7 + 6x + 3$

b) Fully factorise $3x^2 - 6x$

c) Expand and simplify $15 + 6(x - 2)$

8.

a)   Complete the table for the equation $y = 2x + 1$ for values of x between -1 and 4.

x	-1	0	1	2	3	4
y						

b)   Plot the graph of $y = 2x + 1$ on the axes below.

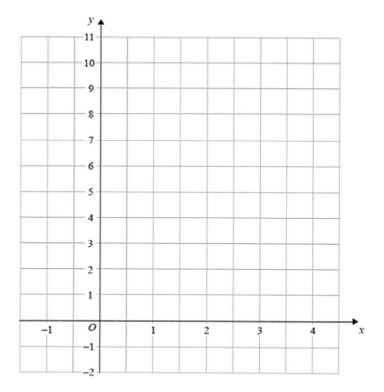

Stretch:

a) Solve both the following inequalities:

$$x + 6 > 9$$
$$3x - 5 < 10$$

b) Find the integer value of x that satisfies both the inequalities

Challenge:

If you have flipped a fair coin 99 times and it has been 'heads' every time, what is the probability of the next coin flip being 'tails'?

Essential 8 Number 8

8A

1. Translate the trapezium by the vector $\begin{pmatrix} -7 \\ 6 \end{pmatrix}$

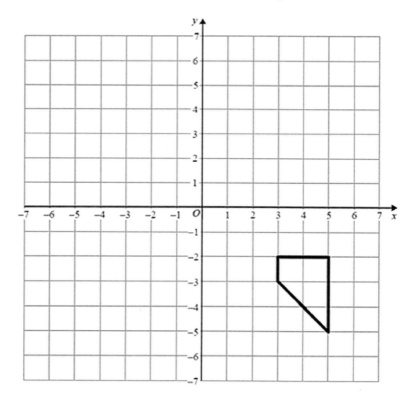

2.

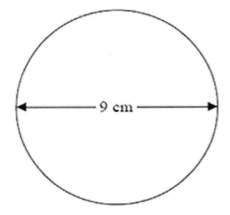

9 cm

Diagram NOT accurately drawn

a) Work out the circumference of the circle.

b) Work out the area of the circle.

3. Here are a 6 sided spinner and a 4 sided spinner. Both are fair.

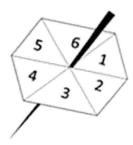 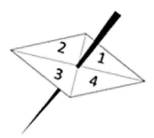

Jane is going to spin each spinner once. Each spinner will land on a number. Jane will add the two numbers to get a score.

a) Complete the possibility space table below for the scores.

	1	2	3	4	5	6
1						
2						
3						
4						

b) What is the probability of her scoring 5?

c) What is the probability of her scoring 7 or more?

d) Which spinner is more likely to land on an odd number?

4.

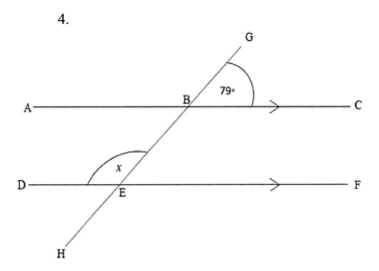

Diagram NOT drawn accurately.

Work out the size of angle x.

Give reasons for your answer.

5.

a) Write 0.8 as a fraction.

b) Write 0.4 as a percentage.

c) Write $\dfrac{12}{16}$ in its simplest form.

6.

Leonardo and Kate share the cost of their Mediterranean cruise in the ratio of 2:3. The cost is 2450 Euros.

How much does Kate pay towards the cost of their cruise?

7.

Simplify

    a) $r + 5r - 2r$

    b) $3mn + 2mn - 4mn$

    c) $3ab \times 7a^3b$

Solve

    d) $4a - 6 = 38$

    e) $\dfrac{72}{f} = 8$

8.

a) Complete the table for the equation $y = 3x + 5$

x	-2	-1	0	1	2	3
y						

b) Plot the graph of $y = 3x + 5$ on the axes below.

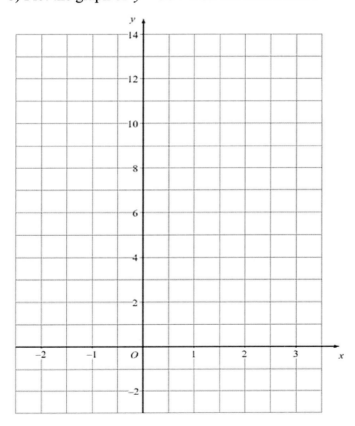

$$a = \begin{pmatrix} 2 \\ -1 \end{pmatrix} \qquad b = \begin{pmatrix} 5 \\ 3 \end{pmatrix}$$

Work out $2b - 3a$ giving your answer as a column vector.

Challenge:

If you place one grain of rice on the first square of a chess board and double the grains of rice on each of the next 63 squares, how many grains will be on the board in total?

Essential 8 Number 9

9A

1.

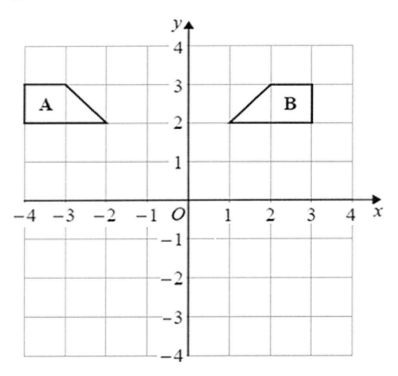

Describe fully the single transformation that maps shape A onto shape B.

*2.

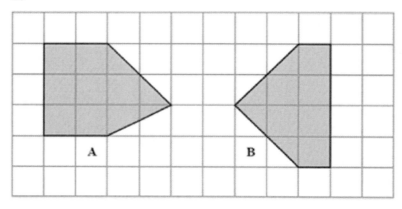

Which shape has the bigger area?

Justify your answer.

3.

A biased spinner has 4 sides and has two blue sections and two red sections.

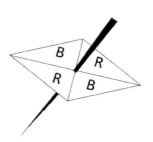

Three friends each spin the biased spinner a number of times.

The table shows the number of times the spinner lands on red and on blue for each of the friends.

	Paul	George	Ringo
Blue	45	89	77
Red	19	46	32

The spinner is to be spun one more time.

(a) Which of the three friends' results will give the best estimate for the probability that the spinner will land on blue? Justify your answer.

Paul says,

"With this spinner you are twice as likely to land on blue as on red."

(b) Is Paul correct?
Justify your answer.

The spinner is to be spun twice.

(c) Use all the results in the table to work out an estimate for the probability that the spinner will land on blue both times.

4.

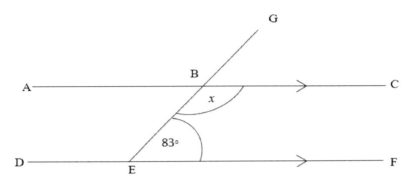

Find angle x.

Explain your answer.

5.

Sam has £3200 in a bank account.

The bank pays 4% interest per annum.

How much will Sam have in his account after a year?

6.

Farah and Rani are primary school teachers.

They share the teaching of a year group which has a total of 60 students.

Farah teaches 25 of them.

What is the ratio of students taught by Farah and Rani?

Give your answer in its simplest form.

7.

a) Expand $2(y + 4)$

b) Expand and simplify $12 + 4(2m - 1)$

c) Factorise $3x + 9$

d) Factorise fully $8c^2d - 2cde$

8.

a) Complete the table for the equation $y = -2x + 6$

x	-2	-1	0	1	2	3
y						

b) Plot the graph of $y = -2x + 6$ on the axes below.

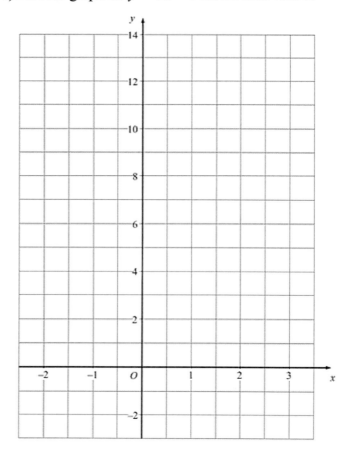

a) Factorise $x^2 + 2x - 8$

b)

Factorise $x^2 - 36$

Challenge:

How many 10p coins can be made to fit round a single 10p coin if they all have to touch the central coin?

Will it be more, fewer or the same amount of 1p coins that can fit exactly around a central 1p coin?

Essential 8 Number 10

10A

1.

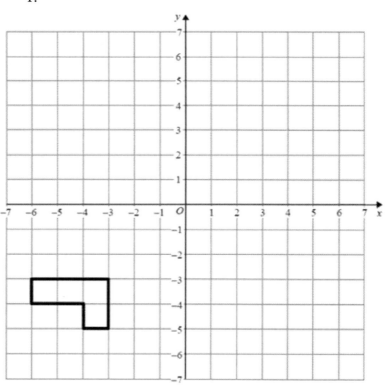

Enlarge the L-shape by scale factor 3 from the centre (-6, -5)

2.

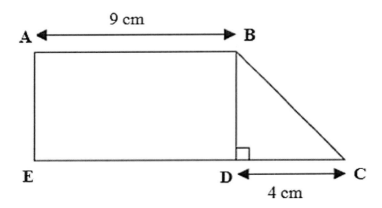

The area of rectangle ABDE is 45 cm².

Work out the area of the trapezium ABCE.

3.

126 people went to the theme park. They chose to go on either the Dodgy Dipper or the Waltzing Wizard rides.

74 of the people were adults

59 of the 126 people went on the Dodgy Dipper

31 of the children went on the Waltzing Wizard

a) Use the information to complete the frequency tree.

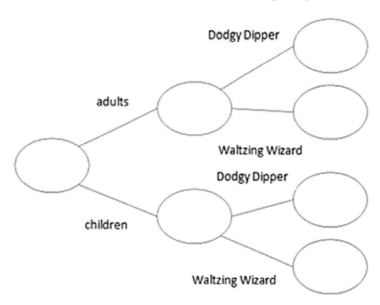

One of the children is chosen at random.

b) Work out the probability that they went on the Dodgy Dipper.

4.

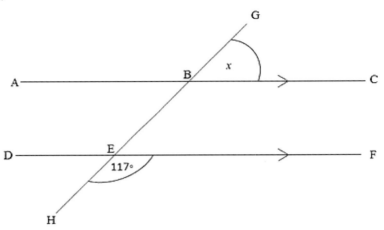

Diagram NOT accurately drawn.

What is angle x?

Justify your answer.

5.

a) Write 0.35 as a fraction.

b) Write 0.07 as a percentage.

c) Write $\dfrac{20}{44}$ in its simplest form.

6.

Louise and Thelma fill their car with petrol. They divide the cost in the ratio of 4:7. Louise pays $44.

How much is the total cost of their petrol?

7.

Simplify

    a) $6pr - 5pr - 2pr$

    b) $\dfrac{6bc \times 9ab}{4c}$

Solve

    c) $-8k = 24$

    d) $\dfrac{v}{4} + 6 = 11$

8.

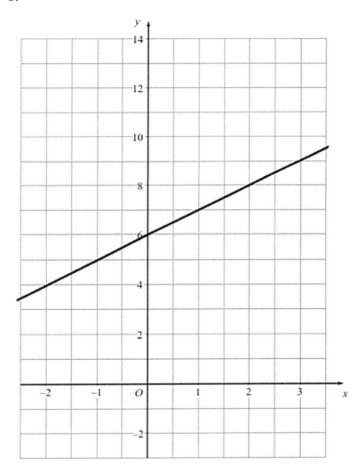

a) What is the gradient of the line?

b) What is the y intercept of the line?

c) Write down the equation of the line in the form $y = mx + c$

The diagram shows a trapezium *ABCD* and two identical semicircles.

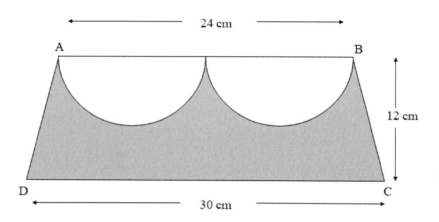

The centre of each semicircle is on *AB*

Work out the area of the shaded region.
Give your answer correct to 3 significant figures.

Challenge:

A gym has 55% more female members than males.

What is the ratio of females to males at the gym?

Essential 8 Number 11

11A

1.

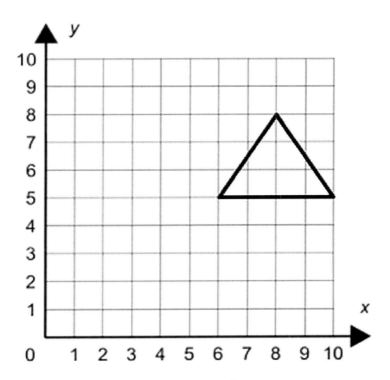

Enlarge the triangle by scale factor $\frac{1}{2}$ centre (2,1)

2.

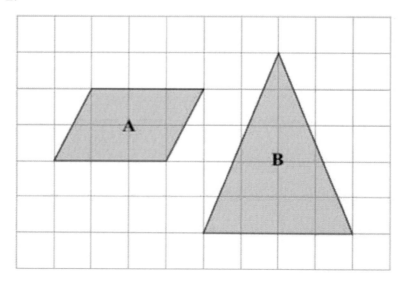

Which has the bigger area, shape A or shape B?

Find the difference in the two areas.

3.

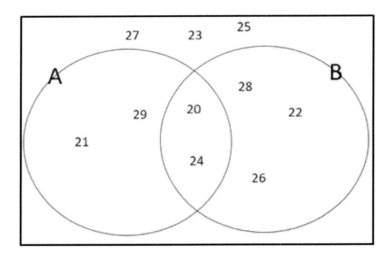

Above is a Venn diagram

Write down the numbers in the set

i) A ∩ B

ii) A ∪ B

One of the numbers in the diagram is chosen at random

b) Find the probability that the number is in set B'

4. Diagram NOT drawn accurately.

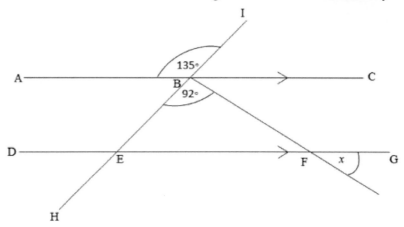

What is angle x?

Justify your answer.

11B

5.

Michael spends 20% of his savings on a television costing £200.
How much money does he now have in his savings account?

6.

Barry, Maurice and Robin are on a survival course. They share 1.6 kg of rice in the ratio 1:4:3.

How much rice does Robin have?

7.

a) Simplify $b + b + b + b$

b) Simplify $3ef + 4ef$

c) Solve $3h + 7 = 13$

d) Factorise $4j - 6$

e) Expand $5(2k - 6)$

8

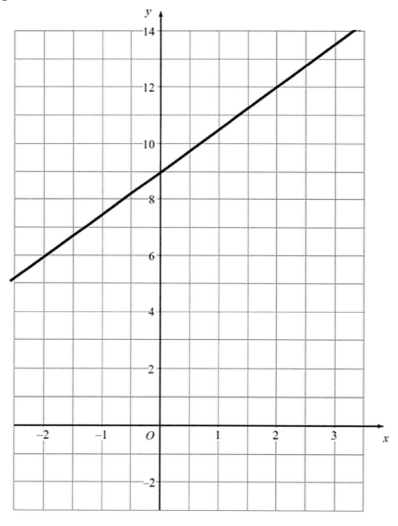

Find the equation of the line in the form of $y = mx + c$

Stretch:

Katie rounds a number, n, to one decimal place.

She writes 8.4

Write down the error interval for n.

Challenge:

In a closing down sale, the shop Sports Unlimited reduced all prices by 50 % .

On the last day of their sale, they reduced all prices by an additional 25% off the half priced items.

What was the equivalent percentage reduction from the original price?

Essential 8 Number 12

12A

1.

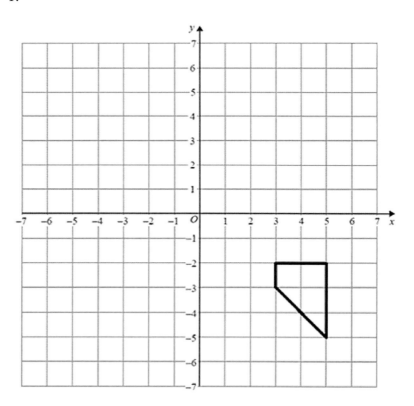

Reflect the quadrilateral in the line $x = y$

2.   Diagram NOT drawn accurately.

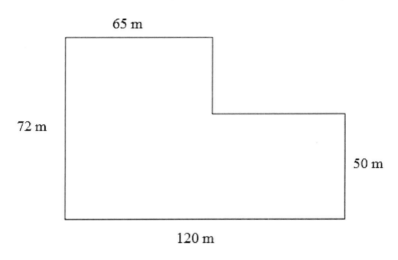

65 m

72 m

50 m

120 m

The diagram above shows the shape and dimensions of Jack's garden.

Jack wants to put fencing around the outside of the garden.

   a) Work out the length of fencing Jack will need.

       The fencing costs £12.50 per metre.

   b) How much will it cost for Jack to buy the fencing?

3.

There are only red, black, green and blue pens in a box.

Frank is going to take a pen at random from the box.

The table shows the probabilities for taking a red or a blue pen.

Colour	Red	Black	Green	Blue
Probability	0.2			0.16

The probability of picking a black pen is the same as a green pen.

a) Complete the table and state the probability that Frank will pick a green pen.

There are 150 pens in the box altogether.

b) How many blue pens are in the box?

4.

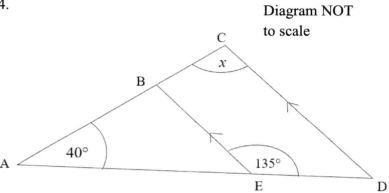

What is angle *x*?

Justify your answer.

5.

a) Express 600 Euros as a percentage of 2000 Euros.

b)   Write 0.45 as a percentage.

c) Write $\dfrac{2}{5}$ as a percentage.

6.

A bouquet is made from roses and lilies in the ratio of 2:3.

There are 10 roses in the bouquet.

How many flowers are there in total in the bouquet?

7.

a) Simplify $c \times c \times c$

b) Solve $4x = 8$

c) Solve $\quad 5q = 2q - 12$

d) Expand $y(4y + 8)$

e) Expand and simplify $\quad (x+2)(x+3)$

8.

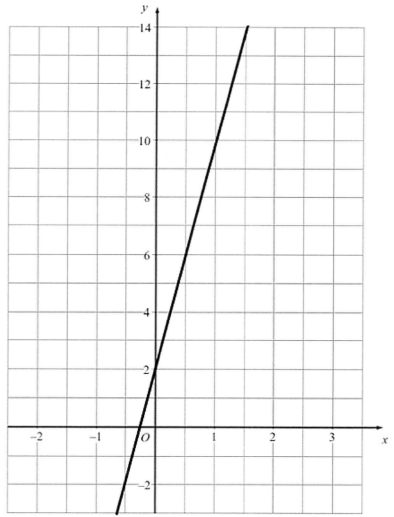

Find the equation of the line in the form of $y = mx + c$

Stretch:

Here are the equations of four straight lines.

Line 1 $y = 3x + 2$

Line 2 $3y = x + 2$

Line 3 $3x + 3y = 2$

Line 4 $3x - y = 2$

Which two of these four lines are parallel?

Line .... and line ....

Challenge:

How many Mondays will there be in the 21st century?